LIVING
ON THE EDGE
SMALL GROUP
STUDY GUIDE

WHY I BELIEVE

Finding Answers To Life's Most Difficult Questions

CHIP INGRAM

Why I Believe

TABLE OF CONTENTS

The fact that you are even reading this page says a lot about you. It says that you are either one of those people that has to read everything, or it says you are open to God using you to lead a group.

Leading a small group can sound intimidating, but it really doesn't have to be. Think of it more as gathering a few friends to get to know each other better and to have some discussion around spiritual matters.

Here are a few practical tips to help you get started:

1. PRAY

   One of the most important principles of spiritual leadership is to realize you can't do this on your own. No matter how long you've been a Christian or been involved in ministry, you need the power of the Holy Spirit. Lean on Him... He will help you.

2. INVITE SOME FRIENDS

   Don't be afraid to ask people to come to your group. You will be surprised how many people are open to a study like this. Whether you have 4 or 14 in your group, it can be a powerful experience. You should probably plan on at least an hour and a half for your group meeting.

3. GET YOUR MATERIALS

   You will need to get a DVD of the video teaching done by Chip Ingram. You can get the DVD from www.livingontheedge.org. Also, it will be helpful for each person to have their own study guide. You can also purchase those through the website.

4. BE PREPARED TO FACILITATE

   Just a few minutes a week in preparation can make a huge difference in the group experience. Each week preview the video teaching and review the discussion questions. If you don't think your group can get through all the questions, select the ones that are most relevant to your group.

5. LEARN TO SAY "I DON'T KNOW"

   This series takes on some of the most difficult questions that Christians and non-Christians struggle with. These sessions will spark some lively and spirited discussions. When tough questions come up, it's ok for you to say "I don't know". Take the pressure off. No one expects you to have all the answers.

6. LOVE YOUR GROUP

   Maybe the most important thing you bring to the group is your personal care for them. If you will pray for them, encourage them, call them, e-mail them, involve them, and love them, God will be pleased and you will have a lot of fun along the way.

Thank you for your availability. May God bless you as you serve Him by serving others.

You are about to begin a powerful journey exploring some of Christianity's toughest questions. This powerful series taught by Chip Ingram provides in depth teaching. This series will help you see that you don't have to throw your brains in the trash to be a Christ follower. You will examine the truth of Christianity and be equipped to intelligently articulate your faith.

Listed below are the segments you will experience each week as well as some hints for getting the most out of this experience. If you are leading the group, you will find some additional help and coaching on page 103.

▲ BEFORE GOD

It is important for us to get "before God" and submit ourselves to his truth. During this section you will watch the video teaching by Chip. He will introduce each session with a personal word to the group followed by the teaching portion of the video. At the end of the teaching segment, Chip will wrap up the session and help the group dive into discussion.

A teaching outline with fill-ins is provided for each session. As you follow along, write down questions or insights that you can share during the discussion time.

Even though most of the verses will appear on the screen and in your notes, it is a great idea to bring your own Bible each week. It will allow you to make notes in your own Bible and find other passages that might be relevant to that week's study.

■ IN COMMUNITY

We not only grow by listening to God's word, but we grow "in community." The friendship and insights of those in the group will enrich your small group experience. Several discussion questions are provided for your group to further engage the teaching content. Keep the following guidelines in mind for having a healthy group discussion.

- **Be involved.** Jump in and share your thoughts. Your ideas are important, and you have a perspective that is unique and can benefit the other group members.

- **Be a good listener.** Value what others are sharing. Seek to really understand the perspective of others in your group and don't be afraid to ask follow up questions.

- **Be courteous.** People hold strong opinions about the topics in this study. Spirited discussion is great. Disrespect and attack is not. When there is disagreement, focus on the issue and never turn the discussion into a personal attack.

- **Be focused.** Stay on topic. Help the group explore the subject at hand, and try to save unrelated questions or stories for afterwards.

- **Be careful not to dominate.** Be aware of the amount of talking you are doing in proportion to the rest of the group, and make space for others to speak.

- **Be a learner.** Stay sensitive to what God might be wanting to teach you through the lesson, as well as through what others have to say. Focus more on your own growth rather than making a point or winning an argument.

ON MISSION

One reason we get "before God" and live "in community" is so that we can be "on mission". Our faith has an external component. We are called to be salt and light by living out our faith in the real world. This section provides some simple suggestions to help the lesson come to life. Don't ignore them; give them a try!

WHY I BELIEVE
IN THE RESURRECTION

Part 1

SESSION 1

Do you have to throw your "brains in the trash" to be a Christ follower?

▲ BEFORE GOD (Watch the Video)

How can someone as well educated and intellectually astute as you appear to be...really believe in a literal Jesus and all this "born-again" stuff?

DR. AL PLATT

The Journey:

Is there intellectually feasible evidence to support a faith in the Jesus of the Bible with His claims of deity, eternal life, and absolute truth?

The Central Issue: The _____

Christianity rises and falls on the truthfulness and reality of the resurrection.

[13]If there is no resurrection of the dead, then not even Christ has been raised. [14]And if Christ has not been raised, our preaching is useless and so is your faith. [15]More than that, we are then found to be false witnesses about God, for we have testified about God that he raised Christ from the dead. But he did not raise him if in fact the dead are not raised. [16]For if the dead are not raised, then Christ has not been raised either. [17]And if Christ has not been raised, your faith is futile; you are still in your sins. [18]Then those also who have fallen asleep in Christ are lost. [19]If only for this life we have hope in Christ, we are of all people most to be pitied.

---

1 CORINTHIANS 15:13-19 (NIV)

8

7 REASONS WHY I BELIEVE IN THE RESURRECTION:

1. The _____ of Jesus of Nazareth is airtight

    • Biblical manuscripts – the quality and quantity

    • 25,000 New Testament documents that authenticate the reality of Jesus Christ

    • Extra Biblical Sources – Josephus, Pliny, Tacitus

    • Archeological confirmation

2. The _____ of Jesus is unquestioned

    • Friend and foe agree – great man, moral teacher

    • Claimed sinless life John 8:46

    • Affirmed by history and impact

3. The _____ of Jesus went unchallenged

    • Fact of miracles, feeding 5000 not disputed

    • Eyewitness accounts validated miracles

    • Acts 2 sermon – even unbelievers acknowledged His works

4. The _____ of Jesus was confirmed

    • By His own claim (John 14:6)

    • By God (Mark 9:7)

    • By His followers (Mark 8:27-30)

    • By His enemies (John 10:33)

The Jews answered Him, "For a good work we do not stone You, but for blasphemy; and because You, being a man, make Yourself out to be God."

JOHN 10:33 (NASB)

- By extra Biblical sources – Pliny A.D. 111
- By fulfillment of over 700 Old Testament prophecies

IN COMMUNITY

1. Share a little of your faith background. Has studying key doctrinal issues been part of your journey or is this all new to you?

2. How comfortable are you having discussions about Christian beliefs? Do you feel confident? Unsure? Equipped? Intimidated?

3. Has there ever been a time when you struggled through your own doubts about the Christian faith? If so, share a little about that journey.

4. Of the four reasons Chip shared for believing in the resurrection, which one is the most compelling to you? Why?

5. Chip said "Christianity rises and falls on the truthfulness and reality of the resurrection." Do you agree with his statement? Why or why not?

6. Read 1 Corinthians 15:13-19. Come up with a list of things Paul says would happen if Jesus DIDN'T rise from the dead.

● ON MISSION

Spend some time this week praying about this series. Ask God to use this series to help you be equipped to explain the claims of Christianity. Then, ask God to give you opportunity to share what you are learning with those who need Christ.

WHY I BELIEVE
IN THE RESURRECTION

Part 2

SESSION 2

BEFORE GOD (Watch the Video)

7 Reasons Why I Believe in the Resurrection (Continued from Session 1)

5. The _____ of Jesus was undisputed

    - At the time by both friend and foe

    - By His flogging, beating, and crucifixion

    - By medical evidence – water and blood indicate puncture of pericardium

    - By burial preparation – 70 pounds of spices and linen

6. The _____ of Jesus was public and secured

    - Joseph of Arimathea's tomb

    - Roman guards

    - Roman seal

    - Size of tombstone – would take 20 men to roll away

    - Penalty of death for guards sleeping

7. The _____ for Jesus' resurrection is convincing

    - Predicted by Old Testament prophets

    - Jesus predicted it openly and numerously

    - Appeared 12 different times to over 500 eye witnesses

    - Appeared in multiple locations and times over 40 days

    - The transformation of the disciples

    - Explosion of the church

    - Inconceivable for disciples to willingly and knowingly "die for a lie"

- Conversion of Saul of Tarsus

- Transformation of Roman empire and the world

- Best legal minds – the evidence is conclusive!

- My testimony – "He changed my life"

What Does This Mean to You?

1. _____ Jesus' claim that he is the way, the truth, and the life.

2. Gives _____ for the future

Because I live, you will live also.

_____

JOHN 14:9 (NIV)

3. It offers spiritual life _____!

¹Now, brothers, I want to remind you of the gospel I preached to you, which you received and on which you have taken your stand. ²By this gospel you are saved, if you hold firmly to the word I preached to you. Otherwise, you have believed in vain.

³For what I received I passed on to you as of first importance: that Christ died for our sins according to the Scriptures, ⁴that he was buried, that he was raised on the third day according to the Scriptures, ⁵and that he appeared to Peter, and then to the Twelve.

⁶After that, he appeared to more than five hundred of the brothers at the same time, most of whom are still living, though some have fallen asleep. ⁷Then he appeared to James, then to all the apostles.

1 CORINTHIANS 15:1-7 (NIV)

Rejecting or accepting the work of Jesus is not an intellectual issue. It is always a moral issue.

▇ IN COMMUNITY

1. If Jesus did indeed rise from the dead, what impact should that have on us? How should it change our behavior?

2. Of all the evidence that Chip shared concerning the resurrection of Jesus, what evidence is most convincing to you?

3. As you hear the evidence for the resurrection, which of the following might be true for you?

    ☐ I am in awe of how much evidence there is for the resurrection of Jesus.

    ☐ This has helped me settle the issue of Christ's resurrection once and for all.

    ☐ I am still not sure what I really believe

    ☐ I can now better articulate why I believe the resurrection of Jesus is a fact of history.

    ☐ I should share my faith with greater confidence and boldness.

4. In 2 Corinthians 4:14 Paul said *because we know that the one who raised the Lord Jesus from the dead will also raise us with Jesus and present us with you to himself.* According to this passage, what does the resurrection have to do with our future?

    _____

    _____

    _____

5. In Ephesians 1:19-20 (NLT) Paul said *[19]I also pray that you will understand the incredible greatness of God's power for us who believe him. This is the same mighty power [20]that raised Christ from the dead and seated him in the place of honor at God's right hand in the heavenly realms.* What does the resurrection have to do with our ability to live the Christian life?

    _____

    _____

    _____

6. One of the evidences Chip shared is the personal testimony of people whose lives have been changed. Have a couple of people in your group briefly share their testimony of how the resurrected Christ has changed their life.

● ON MISSION

This week seek to be conscious of living in the power of the resurrection. To help you, meditate on and memorize Ephesians 1:19-20 (NLT).

> [19]I also pray that you will understand the incredible greatness of God's power for us who believe him. This is the same mighty power [20]that raised Christ from the dead and seated him in the place of honor at God's right hand in the heavenly realms.

> EPHESIANS 1:19-20 (NLT)

Why is the resurrection important?

"If Christ has not been raised," wrote Paul, the apostle, "our preaching is useless and so is your faith." Harsh words, perhaps. And yet, according to Paul, the resurrection is not optional. There is no other name under heaven by which one can be saved, and no other method of salvation other than belief in and identification with Jesus' death, burial, resurrection and ascension. Jesus, raised from the dead, is the center of the Christian faith, the basis for the global Christian church, and the hope for personal salvation and eternal life.

However, as scholars, theologians and even journalists have noted, not a day has passed in the last two millennia when this fundamental claim has not been questioned.[1] From the very first days, any suggestion that Jesus' physical body was raised from the dead was confronted with skepticism and criticism. Most Jews continued waiting for the promised Messiah, and any proposition that their wait had ended was outrageous and even blasphemous. "How could a lowly Galilean peasant who died a criminal's death – and failed to put even a dent in the Roman oppression of Israel – have anything in common with God's Messiah?" The Romans, mostly for political reasons, attempted to repudiate the movement to prevent incursion against their swelling empire. And Greeks, including many "Gnostic" Christians, rejected the concept of a resurrected body, preferring instead the dualistic view that Jesus' life on earth was material, but after death, only his spirit moved on to the heavenly dwelling. From all sides, it seems, people resisted the notion that a physical, bodily resurrection was not only possible, but had happened.

And that resistance continues today. In the past few centuries, with the advent of progressive historical, archeological and textual fields of study, the Bible and its claim of resurrection continues to be the subject of intense criticism. One of the most public and critical assessments has come from a group called the *Jesus Seminar*. Begun in the mid-1980's, this association of Bible scholars "was organized to discover and report a scholarly consensus on the historical authenticity of the sayings and events attributed to Jesus in the gospels."[2] In their collective reconstruction of the historical Jesus, they conclude, "a mortal man born of two human parents, Jesus did not perform nature miracles, die as a substitute for sinners nor rise bodily from the dead. Sightings of a risen Jesus were nothing more than the visionary experiences of some of his disciples rather than physical encounters."[3] Indeed, in their estimation, we can be confident in the historical reliability of less than 20% of the New Testament.[4]

---

[1] http://www.newsweek.com/1996/04/07/rethinking-the-resurrection.html
[2] http://www.westarinstitute.org/Seminars/seminars.html
[3] http://www.facebook.com/pages/Jesus-Seminar/113028455377657
[4] http://www.westarinstitute.org/Seminars/phase2.html

Building on this ardent skepticism is a new band of critics called the *New Atheists*. Led by notable scientists, philosophers and journalists such as biologist Richard Dawkins and author Christopher Hitchens, they excoriate anyone who attempts to defend miracles in any and every sense. According to Dawkins, "The Virgin Birth, the Resurrection, the raising of Lazarus, even the Old Testament miracles, all are freely used for religious propaganda, and they are very effective with an audience of unsophisticates and children." He continues: "Accounts of Jesus' resurrection and ascension are about as well-documented as Jack and the Beanstalk." While advocates for the *Jesus Seminar* state that belief in the resurrection is intellectually misguided and a burden to our contemporary understanding of Jesus' life and message, the New Atheists take a harder line, suggesting that belief in fables like the resurrection is perhaps one of the greatest threats to civil life.

So, given these seemingly ubiquitous criticisms, why is the resurrection important?

However, as stated above, the evidence that Jesus lived, died, and was resurrected is convincing. The only written evidence we have of this event, the New Testament, provides two indicators to the resurrection: Jesus' empty tomb and his various post-resurrection appearances. And corroborating this data are three historical and experiential observations:

1. Neither the Roman government nor the Jewish establishment could produce Jesus' body. This one act would have easily squashed the movement.

2. People don't knowingly die for a lie. How could the early believers transform from cowards to martyrs overnight, unless they actually believed what they said?

3. The explosion of the early church, in the face of unprecedented persecution, seems unlikely unless there was more to it than wishful thinking on the part of a small anonymous band of peasants.[5]

The reality is we most likely have all the information we'll ever have about Jesus' life, death and the subsequent events, contained in the Scriptures.

In the end, what matters is not only what happened nearly 2,000 years ago, but its implications for today. Christianity boldly states that those in Christ can expect their own resurrection from the dead, and life with God for eternity.

---

[5] Incidentally, it is notable that in Matthew's account, women were the first eye-witnesses to the empty tomb and the risen Christ. If the writer were fabricating this story, clearly this is not the most compelling argument. Because women carried little authority or credibility in this culture, it would have been far more convincing to note that men were the first witnesses.

Recommended Reading List:

1. Tim Keller, *The Reason for God: Belief in an Age of Skepticism.* (chapter 13)

2. Lee Strobel, *The Case for the Resurrection: A First-Century Investigative Reporter Probes History's Pivotal Event.*

3. N.T. Wright, *The Resurrection of the Son of God.*

4. William Lane Craig, *Reasonable Faith: Christian Truth and Apologetics.* (especially chapter 8)

WHY I BELIEVE
IN LIFE AFTER DEATH

Part 1

SESSION 3

Evidences for an Afterlife:

1. _____

> *"I'm not sure what's after death, but nature seems to give us a picture of what it will be like, some new kind of life after death."*
>
> _____
> PLATO

2. _____

Every culture believes in a life after death

3. _____

4. _____

5. _____

6. _____ – "Near Death Experiences"

7. _____ and the Bible

In history, Jesus is the only religious leader who claims to have died and come back to life.

Conclusion:

The cumulative evidence makes belief in an afterlife the most rational, plausible, and intellectually defensible conclusion to the question..."*Is there life after death?*"

What Does the Bible Teach about the Afterlife?

Four Summary Statements:

1. At death, every person's soul/spirit enters _____

    _____ into _____.

    • Jesus' Paradigm of the Afterlife

    [19]"*There was a rich man who was dressed in purple and fine linen and lived in luxury every day.* [20]*At his gate was laid a beggar named Lazarus, covered with sores* [21]*and longing to eat what fell from the rich man's table. Even the dogs came and licked his sores.*

    [22]"*The time came when the beggar died and the angels carried him to Abraham's side. The rich man also died and was buried.* [23]*In Hades, where he was in torment, he looked up and saw Abraham far away, with Lazarus by his side.* [24]*So he called to him, 'Father Abraham, have pity on me and send Lazarus to dip the tip of his finger in water and cool my tongue, because I am in agony in this fire.'*

    [25]"*But Abraham replied, 'Son, remember that in your lifetime you received your good things, while Lazarus received bad things, but now he is comforted here and you are in agony.* [26]*And besides all this, between us and you a great chasm has been set in place, so that those*

who want to go from here to you cannot, nor can anyone cross over from there to us.'

²⁷"He answered, 'Then I beg you, father, send Lazarus to my family, ²⁸for I have five brothers. Let him warn them, so that they will not also come to this place of torment.'

²⁹"Abraham replied, 'They have Moses and the Prophets; let them listen to them.'

³⁰""No, father Abraham,' he said, 'but if someone from the dead goes to them, they will repent.'

³¹"He said to him, 'If they do not listen to Moses and the Prophets, they will not be convinced even if someone rises from the dead.'"

LUKE 16:19-31 (NIV)

- Paul's Paradigm of the Afterlife

¹For we know that if the earthly tent we live in is destroyed, we have a building from God, an eternal house in heaven, not built by human hands. ²Meanwhile we groan, longing to be clothed instead with our heavenly dwelling, ³because when we are clothed, we will not be found naked. ⁴For while we are in this tent, we groan and are burdened, because we do not wish to be unclothed but to be clothed instead with our heavenly dwelling, so that what is mortal may be swallowed up by life. ⁵Now the one who has fashioned us for this very purpose is God, who has given us the Spirit as a deposit, guaranteeing what is to come.

⁶Therefore we are always confident and know that as long as we are at home in the body we are away from the Lord. ⁷For we live by faith, not by sight. ⁸We are

confident, I say, and would prefer to be away from the body and at home with the Lord.

---

2 CORINTHIANS 5:1-8 (NIV)

2. Every person will one day be resurrected and

_____.

¹⁴However, I admit that I worship the God of our ancestors as a follower of the Way, which they call a sect. I believe everything that is in accordance with the Law and that is written in the Prophets, ¹⁵and I have the same hope in God as these men themselves have, that there will be a resurrection of both the righteous and the wicked.

ACTS 24:14-15 (NIV)

¹¹Then I saw a great white throne and him who was seated on it. The earth and the heavens fled from his presence, and there was no place for them. ¹²And I saw the dead, great and small, standing before the throne, and books were opened. Another book was opened, which is the book of life. The dead were judged according to what they had done as recorded in the books. ¹³The sea gave up the dead that were in it, and death and Hades gave up the dead that were in them, and each person was judged according to what they had done.

REVELATION 20:11-13 (NIV)

3. Every person will be _____ and granted the "extended capacity" to fulfill in eternity the deepest yearnings and desires of their hearts while on earth.

Just as people are destined to die once, and after that to face judgment.

HEBREWS 9:27 (NIV)

[25]Very truly I tell you, a time is coming and has now come when the dead will hear the voice of the Son of God and those who hear will live. [26]For as the Father has life in himself, so he has granted the Son also to have life in himself. [27]And he has given him authority to judge because he is the Son of Man.

JOHN 5:25-27 (NIV)

4. Every person will spend eternity in _____ with Christ and fellow believers, or in _____ separated from God forever.

■ IN COMMUNITY

1. What was your gut level response as you listened to the teaching in this session?

2. If the Bible's teaching on the afterlife is really true how would it change your priorities? Decisions you make? The way you treat people?

3. How much time do you spend thinking about the afterlife? How can thinking about the afterlife be helpful and positive for a Christ follower?

4. Read Luke 16:19-31. As a group, come up with a list of truths we learn from this passage about the afterlife.

5. Read 2 Corinthians 5:1-8. How should the truth of this passage impact how we live and view our earthly life?

6. 1 Peter 2:11-12 says *Dear friends, I urge you, as aliens and strangers in the world, to abstain from sinful desires, which war against your soul. Live such good lives among the pagans that, though they accuse you of doing wrong, they may see your good deeds and glorify God on the day he visits us.* How does seeing ourselves as strangers in the world help us to abstain from sinful desires?

_____

_____

_____

● ON MISSION

This week spend some time thinking about what it means to live as a citizen of heaven. Then, make a list of implications for your life.

WHY I BELIEVE
IN LIFE AFTER DEATH

Part 2

SESSION 4

Evidences For An Afterlife (Continued from Session 3)

> *Then they will go away to eternal punishment, but the righteous to eternal life.*

MATTHEW 25:46 (NIV)

> *Very truly I tell you, whoever hears my word and believes him who sent me has eternal life and will not be judged but has crossed over from death to life.*

JOHN 5:24 (NIV)

Eternal life doesn't begin in heaven. Eternal life begins the moment we believe.

A Preview of Heaven – The Great Adventure:

- _____ is there

> *[1]Then I saw "a new heaven and a new earth," for the first heaven and the first earth had passed away, and there was no longer any sea. [2]I saw the Holy City, the new Jerusalem, coming down out of heaven from God, prepared as a bride beautifully dressed for her husband. [3]And I heard a loud voice from the throne saying, "Look! God's dwelling place is now among the people, and he will dwell with them. They will be his people, and God*

himself will be with them and be their God. ⁴'He will wipe every tear from their eyes. There will be no more death' or mourning or crying or pain, for the old order of things has passed away."

⁵He who was seated on the throne said, "I am making everything new!" Then he said, "Write this down, for these words are trustworthy and true."

REVELATION 21:1-5 (NIV)

• Beauty, Light, Warmth

¹Then the angel showed me the river of the water of life, as clear as crystal, flowing from the throne of God and of the Lamb ²down the middle of the great street of the city. On each side of the river stood the tree of life, bearing twelve crops of fruit, yielding its fruit every month. And the leaves of the tree are for the healing of the nations. ³No longer will there be any curse. The throne of God and of the Lamb will be in the city, and his servants will serve him. ⁴They will see his face, and his name will be on their foreheads. ⁵There will be no more night. They will not need the light of a lamp or the light of the sun, for the Lord God will give them light. And they will reign for ever and ever.

REVELATION 22:1-5

- Wonderful Relationships — Hebrews 12:22-24

- Incredible Accommodations — John 14:1-3

- A Fresh Start

  - A New Nature — 1 John 3:2

  - A New Body — 2 Corinthians 5:1-5

  - A New Vocation — Revelation 22:5; 1 Corinthians 6:3

- Various Levels of Reward — 2 Corinthians 5:10

- Complete Rest, Protection, Contentment, Security, Peace, Purpose, and Rest — Revelation 21-22

- Unbridled Joy, Celebration, Worship, Laughter, and Music — Matthew 26:29; Revelation 21-22

- Learning, Growing, Fellowship, Worshipping, Serving, Eating, and Discovering the Infinite Majesty of God and His Universe (yet unrevealed to us) — Revelation 5:8-9; Revelation 21-22

- Forever — Revelation 22:5

A Preview of Hell – The Horrible Choice:

- God is _____ there

They will be punished with everlasting destruction and shut out from the presence of the Lord and from the glory of his might.

2 THESSALONIANS 1:9 (NIV)

- Punishment and Torment — Revelation 14:10-11

- Varying Degrees of Punishment — Matthew 11:21-24

- Outer Darkness — Matthew 8:12

- Weeping — Matthew 8:12

- Wailing — Matthew 13:40-42

- Gnashing of Teeth — Luke 13:28

- Forever — Hebrews 6:2, Revelation 14:11

Why There Must Be A Hell:

- Man's Dignity and _____ demand a Hell.

- God's Holiness and _____ demand a Hell.

- Sin's seriousness demands a Hell.

- Evil's _____ demand a Hell.

Conclusion:

Will your eternal future be a blissful adventure or a horrible choice?

■ IN COMMUNITY

1. Break into groups of two. Practice sharing the good news of salvation. Who do you know that needs Christ? Could you see yourself having a God conversation with them about their need for Christ?

_____

_____

_____

2. When you were growing up, was hell talked about and what was your church's or family's view of hell?

_____

_____

_____

3. Why do you think hell is almost never preached about and rarely talked about among Christians today?

_____

_____

_____

4. In I Corinthians 2:9-10 Paul writes:

[9]However, as it is written: "What no eye has seen, what no ear has heard, and what no human mind has conceived" — the things God has prepared for those who love him — [10]these are the things God has revealed to us by his Spirit.

For you personally, what about heaven most excited you?

_____

_____

_____

5. Read Revelation 21:1-4, 22-27 and Revelation 22:1-5. As a group come up with a list of things that we can learn from these passages about heaven.

6. In 1 Corinthians 3:10-15 Paul talks about the judgment of rewards in heaven. As believers our sins have already been paid for, so this judgment is like a rewards ceremony for all believers. As you read this passage, what most stands out to you regarding our future judgment of rewards?

● ON MISSION

Spend some time reflecting this week on the reality of heaven and hell. Let this week's session drive you to pray for and maybe talk to a friend who does not know Christ.

Why is the afterlife important?

> "At the age of ten, Elizabeth Maxim found herself floating above her own body as ER staff tried to decide what to do. She was pulled back only to descend into a coma. Hours later, while undergoing brain surgery for a ruptured aneurysm, she died again. Only this time, she found herself surrounded by loving energies and communicating with God... Blind and paralyzed [after being revived a second time], Elizabeth's physical recovery was set against a backdrop of spiritual confusion and continuous celestial contact..."[6]

Believe it or not, Elizabeth's near death experience is not uncommon. Nor is her confusion from trying to assemble the fragments of information and experiences into a coherent view of what happens after one dies. A simple search of the available books and articles on the afterlife will yield a tsunami of literature addressing the topic. So, obviously, the afterlife is at least a popular topic. But what makes it important?

Well, there's no denying that belief in an afterlife – whatever form it takes – is convenient. After all, who wants death to be the end? Game over! Finished! Done-for! Not many folks eagerly anticipate this conclusion to their 70 or 80 years on earth. But that discomfort alone cannot make the potential for an afterlife true. A clue, perhaps—but not necessarily true.[7] And yet, because the death rate continues to hover around 100%, the afterlife will likely always be an issue of intense focus, discussion, study, and prognostication.

In fact, most cultures throughout all times have had some sense that death was not the end. Ancient Egyptian culture provides one of the earliest and most extensive theories on the afterlife. They believed that physical death was a brief hiatus of an eternal existence. Through obedience to the gods, proper burial (ie. mummification), and adequate supplies to accompany them on their post-death journey, the assumption was that one could achieve a desirable and rewarding afterlife.

Ancient Roman and Greek culture had a similarly robust theology of the afterlife. In Greek mythology, Hermes was the messenger god who delivered people's post-death souls to the underworld, where they would be evaluated

---

[6] From the back cover of *After Here: The Celestial Plane and What Happens When We Die*, Elizabeth Maxim's exploration of the afterlife.

[7] C.S. Lewis, in his book *Mere Christianity*, famously wrote, "If I find in myself a desire which no experience in this world can satisfy, the most probable explanation is that I was made for another world." (p. 137)

for how they lived their lives – the good received paradise, and the bad were delivered to a place of eternal torment.

Hinduism's – and, for the most part, Buddhism's – view of the afterlife varies from these mostly western ancient forms in that one does not leave this earth until they have achieved enough good deeds, or karma, to be united with god. Until then, they are reincarnated as another life form time and again, according to the moral value of their cumulative actions. If bad karma outweighs the good, one is reborn in animal form or even other lower creatures. If good karma outweighs the bad, one is reborn as a human. Consequently, ones physical body is nothing but a shell for the soul, which continues on through the cycle of birth, life, death and rebirth, until hopefully and finally escaping the cycle and becoming one with god.

Given these examples, belief in the afterlife has been a defining characteristic of both ancient and modern cultures. However, in the last few hundred years, a movement to counter these viewpoints is gaining momentum. Operating under the monikers of Humanists, Materialists, or Naturalists, many people believe that the "promises of immortal salvation or fear of eternal damnation are both illusory and harmful. They distract humans from present concerns, from self-actualization, and from rectifying social injustices. Modern science discredits such historic concepts... Rather, science affirms that the human species is an emergence from natural evolutionary forces... There is no credible evidence that life survives the death of the body. We continue to exist in our progeny and in the way that our lives have influenced others in our culture."[8] In other words, because this life is all there is, we should do our best to live good lives so that we leave a positive legacy and memory – nothing more and nothing less.

But, while life after death cannot be proven beyond the shadow of a doubt, so much runs counter to these naturalist/humanist/materialist assumptions. Even setting a theistic viewpoint aside, too much seems to indicate the exact opposite. Nature, for example, suggests that death is but a hiatus in the cycle of ongoing life. Autumn leads to winter, and winter leads to spring, which yields the subsequent "rebirth" of various life forms.[9] An acorn falls from an ancient oak tree and creates another oak tree. A caterpillar spins a cocoon, and crawls inside, only to later emerge as a butterfly. Practically everything around us illustrates this ongoing cycle of life.

Similarly, psychologists have identified an innate, unquenchable inner longing for something more out of life. No matter what one accomplishes or achieves,

---

[8] Excerpts from the second affirmation in the *Humanist Manifesto II*, signed by thousands of scholars and academic leaders.
[9] Even Plato, the famous Greek philosopher, concluded that nature suggests some form of life after death.

there's almost always a sense that we're "not there yet." The writer of the book of Ecclesiastes argues that this is because God has placed eternity in our hearts. But whatever the reason, these longings seem to be shadows of a life beyond this life.

Even our sense of justice points to the existence of a time or place of resolution. "Life isn't fair," we tell our children. And yet, for some reason, each of us desires fairness. We long for "good people" to get their due, and "bad people" to be paid back in full. But, since this life doesn't always seem to compensate for our actions, it's only logical that there would be a continuation where the scales are balanced.

Perhaps the most interesting data, however, comes from near death experiences. Though these accounts vary wildly in their testimony, the shared elements suggest that when one's brain waves flatline and heart stops, their awareness doesn't necessarily end. Indeed, thousands of people would tell quite the opposite story—that at the time of death, they had never felt more fully alive.

And the Christian Bible validates this claim. John 10:10 quotes Jesus as saying, "I have come that they may have life, and have it to the full." And in the context of John's great emphasis on eternal life, we can deduce that Jesus was talking about more than 70 years of contentment or satisfaction; he was talking about fullness of life everlasting. So, like other religions, both ancient and modern, Jesus and the New Testament writers concur that this life is not all there is to this life.[10] That after death, all people will stand judgment for their actions on earth.[11]

So, is the afterlife important? Yes. Because, if everybody spends eternity somewhere, then it behooves each one of us to understand what lies on the other side of death, and what is required to be there. And while most religions base one's standing in the afterlife on our actions here on earth,[12] Christianity alone bases it on God's act in sending Christ to be the way, the truth and the life.

---

[10] See Matthew 25:46 and Acts 24:14-15.

[11] Of course, one major differentiator (and maybe THE major differentiator) between Christianity and other religions is that Jesus has actually suffered the consequences of sin for those who've trusted him. While in other religions, people are held accountable for their actions, Christians are judged through the righteousness of Christ. And only on account of his righteousness, are they reconciled to a perfect, holy and righteous God.

[12] It has been said that "Religion is man's attempt to reach God, but Jesus is God's attempt to reach man."

Recommended Reading List:

1. N.T. Wright, *Surprised By Hope*.

2. Dinesh D'Souza, *Life After Death*.

3. Jeffrey Long and Paul Perry, *Evidence of the Afterlife: The Science of Near-Death Experiences*.

WHY I BELIEVE
IN THE BIBLE

Part 1

SESSION 5

Is it intellectually feasible to believe the Bible really is God's Word?

Five Crucial Questions About the Bible:

1. Is the Bible the word of men or the very words of God?

2. Is the Bible full of myths, legends, and fairytales, or historically reliable?

3. Is ALL of the Bible true and trustworthy or only parts of it?

4. Can a Bible that has been translated so many times for so many hundreds of years still be accurate?

5. What makes the Bible so different than all other religious writings and their claims to truth?

7 Reasons Why I Believe in the Bible:

1. _____ – The Bible is a historically accurate document.

   • Hittite Civilization Discovered

   • The Black Stele

   • Solomon's horse stables

   • Luke – New Testament – Sir William Ramsey's Work

"No archeological discovery has ever controverted a biblical reference. Scores of archeological findings have been made which confirm in clear outline or in exact detail historical statements."

DR. NELSON GLUECK
AUTHORITY ON ISRAELI ARCHEOLOGY

2. _____ – The Bible claims to infallibly reveal the very words and mind of God.

- *"All Scripture is God breathed..."* 2 Timothy 3:16

- Old Testament sayings are referred to as Scripture — 1 Timothy 5:18

- *"...Paul also wrote you with the wisdom that God gave him."* — 2 Peter 3:16

- 3,000 inferences of Divine authority

3. _____ – The Bible's unity, structure, and subject matter argue for a supernatural authorship.

- 40 authors, 3 languages, 1,500 years

- Central theme is Jesus Christ

- 2 billion publications since 1455

- Who would write such an honest account (even unfavorable) of themselves? i.e. David, Moses, Solomon, Paul

4. _____ – believed the Old Testament to be the very words of God and predicted the New Testament to be likewise.

- Not "concepts" or portions, but the actual words are "God-breathed"

- The scope of the whole Old Testament-- Matthew 5:17-18

- Jesus' view of the resurrection is based on the tense of a verb Jesus replied:

29"You are in error because you do not know the Scriptures or the power of God. 30At the resurrection people will neither marry nor be given in marriage; they will be like the angels in heaven. 31But about the resurrection of the dead—have you not read what God said to you, 32'I am the God of Abraham, the God of Isaac, and the God of Jacob'? He is not the God of the dead but of the living."

MATTHEW 22:29-32 (NIV)

- Paul's argument based on plural vs. singular use of "seed"

The promises were spoken to Abraham and to his seed. Scripture does not say "and to seeds," meaning many people, but "and to your seed," meaning one person, who is Christ.

GALATIANS 3:16 (NIV)

■ IN COMMUNITY

1. If someone asked you, "do you really believe the Bible?" what would you tell them? What is the number one reason you believe the Bible really is God's Word?

2. When you were growing up, what was your family's view of the Bible?

3. Of the 4 reasons for believing the Bible that Chip shared in this session, which one is the most compelling to you? Why?

4. 2 Timothy 3:16 says that "all Scripture is God-breathed..." If someone asked you to explain that phrase, what would you say?

5. Why is Jesus' view of Scripture important in establishing the credibility of the Bible?

    _____

    _____

    _____

6. Chip talked about the actual words of the Bible being inspired, not just the concepts. Why is believing that only the concepts are inspired a "slippery slope"?

    _____

    _____

    _____

● ON MISSION
_____

This week work on memorizing 2 Timothy 3:16-17 (NIV)

> *All Scripture is God-breathed and is useful for teaching, rebuking, correcting and training in righteousness, so that the servant of God may be thoroughly equipped for every good work.*
>
> _____
>
> **2 TIMOTHY 3:16-17 (NIV)**

WHY I BELIEVE
IN THE BIBLE

Part 2

SESSION 6

7 Reasons Why I Believe The Bible (Continued from session 5)

5. _____ – sets the Bible apart from all other religious writings

> *⁹Remember the former things, those of long ago; I am God, and there is no other; I am God, and there is none like me. ¹⁰I make known the end from the beginning, from ancient times, what is still to come. I say, 'My counsel will stand, and I will do all my pleasure.'*

ISAIAH 46:9-10 (NIV)

- Judgment of Tyre — Ezekiel 26

- Succession of World Empires — Daniel 2, 7

- Fulfillment of Jesus as Messiah — 300 Predictions

The probability of 8 predictions coming true = 1 out of 10 to the 17th

PETER STONER, SCIENCE SPEAKS

6. _____ – The Bible's purity and perseverance throughout the centuries is nothing short of miraculous

- Meticulous Precision of Copyists When Transcribing

- Proximity of Manuscripts

  - Plato — earliest copy about 900AD (1200 years after writing — there are 7 copies

  - Aristotle — earliest copy 1100AD (1400 years after writing)

  - Homer — earliest copy 400BC (500 years after writing)

  - New Testament — earliest copy 125AD (25-75 years after writing)

  - There are 24,643 manuscripts or pieces of manuscripts of the New Testament

- Dead Sea Scrolls

7. _____ – The Bible's power to transform lives and nations is overwhelmingly documented

Words about the Word

- Joshua 1:8

- Jeremiah 15:16

- Psalm 119:9, 11

- Matthew 4:4

- 1 Peter 2:2

- Hebrews 4:12

Your Response – 3 Challenges:

FOR SKEPTIC:

I am willing to examine the evidence to my honest questions about the Bible.

FOR QUESTIONING CHRISTIAN:

I am willing to read the New Testament and make up my own mind concerning the Bible.

FOR COMMITTED CHRIST FOLLOWER:

I am committing to read, study, and develop personal convictions about how I will live my life and relate to others.

■ IN COMMUNITY

1. Complete the following statement: "Right now my personal relationship to the Bible is..."

2. What stood out to you from the teaching in this session? Why?

3. Chip listed 30 prophecies that have been fulfilled in Jesus. In your opinion, what prophecy made about Jesus is the most remarkable?

4. Psalms 119:9-11 (NIV) says

    By living according to Your Word. I seek you with all my heart; do not let me stray from your commands. I have hidden Your Word in my heart that I might not sin against you.

    How can a young person stay on the path of purity?

    _____

    _____

    _____

    In what specific ways has the Word of God shaped how you live (i.e. convictions and behavior)?

    _____

    _____

    _____

5. Share how God has spoken to you through his Word in recent weeks.

    _____

    _____

    _____

6. Chip closed by reading the following verses:

- Joshua 1:8
- Jeremiah 15:16
- Psalm 119:9, 11
- Matthew 4:4
- 1 Peter 2:2
- Hebrews 4:12

Which of these verses is the one you most need to hear today?

_____

_____

_____

● ON MISSION

If you are still exploring Christianity or still have questions, take Chip's challenge to read through the New Testament. Ask God to speak to you and commit to being obedient to what he shows you.

For those in the group who have settled your view of Scripture, select a passage or even chapter of Scripture to memorize.

Why is the reliability of the Bible important?

For nearly 2,000 years, the Bible's authority, reliability and status as God's written word was a foregone conclusion throughout most of the world. However, in the last two centuries, with the invention of the scientific method, higher criticism[1], literary criticism[2], and various archaeological hypotheses – not to mention a strong bias against the supernatural – that is no longer the case. One could argue that in our day and age, the default assumption is that the burden of proof lies with those who believe the Bible is an authoritative and reliable book to make their case, rather than the other way around.

In fact, any book that makes absolute moral and theological assertions is likely to make many people uncomfortable. When faced with a challenge to one's viewpoint, lifestyle, or desires, most people in our culture naturally bristle and look for alternative explanations. And often, at least regarding the Christian Bible, this aversion is expressed through intellectual objections, such as:

- **Inspiration**: The Bible is simply a collection of human words; good ones, perhaps. But nothing more than man's opinions about how to live.

- **Historicity**: The Bible is full of myths, legends and fairytales. To consider it historical and useful today is to deny the obvious.

- **Entirety**: Some of the Bible can be useful, but much of it cannot. Therefore, we must pick and choose what's valuable, and discard the rest.

- **Exclusivity**: Since the core message of the Bible is no different than other holy books', it's arrogant to suggest that the Bible is THE way to know God.

- **Plausibility**: Because the Bible contains stories of the supernatural, and I do not believe in miracles, the Bible cannot be reliable or authoritative.

The result of objections like these is obvious:

The Bible becomes nothing more than an impotent, ancient, largely irrelevant document that is useful only when it serves our needs.

---

[1] Studies which attempt to establish the authorship, date, and place of composition of an ancient text by comparing it to other contemporary texts.

[2] Scholarly attempts to identify and remove copy errors in the text of an ancient manuscript.

The only problem is that common sense and the Bible itself won't allow for this convenient arrangement. First, within its pages are claims to inspiration, such as when Paul proposes that all Scripture is God-breathed. Second, the Bible also diligently and accurately records a historical record that has been studied and corroborated to the point that Dr. Nelson Glueck, one of the last century's leading archaeologists, would contend, "It may be stated categorically that no archaeological discovery has ever controverted a Biblical reference."[4] Third, the assertion that we get to "pick and choose" what's valuable and discard the rest is simply intellectually dishonest. Paul not only argued that the entirety of Scripture is God-breathed,[3] but also that it's "useful for teaching, rebuking, correcting and training in righteousness." That I dislike something the Bible says might make it unpleasant, but does not make it untrue. Fourth, since the Bible's message is categorically different than every other holy book, the two most important questions are, "Is what it says true?" and "Do you believe it?" It is *exclusive* to say that 2+2 does not equal 5; but it is not arrogant to do so. And finally, to dismiss the Bible as implausible because it contains supernatural events is evidence of one's prejudice, but has no bearing on its authenticity or validity.

In the end, the reliability of the Bible is important because if we are to discover what the Scriptures really say, and attempt to live consistently with its moral, ethical and theological demands, we must be able to respond to and even reject a variety of objections. And the great thing is that Christians do not have to be bashful in their faith, but rather can be confident in the historical reliability and trustworthiness of that which the Psalmist says, "is more precious to me than thousands of pieces of silver and gold."

---

[3] 2 Timothy 3:16. While it can be argued that this is a circular reference, the fact that 40 authors, from different places, and writing over the span of 1,500+ years, somehow agree on the overriding theme of Bible is miraculous, in and of itself.

[4] Glueck, Nelson. Rivers in the Desert, (New York: Farrar, Strous and Cudahy, 1959), p. 136. Add to this fact that the Gospels, alone, are by far the most well documented and preserved ancient text in all of ancient history.

Recommended Reading List:

1. N.T. Wright, The Last Word.

2. Eugene Peterson, Eat This Book.

3. Craig Blomberg, The Reliability of the Gospels.

4. Bart Ehrman, Jesus, Interrupted. Revealing the Hidden Contradictions in the Bible (And Why We Don't Know About Them). (This is a good book to read to understand an opposing view.)

WHY I BELIEVE
IN CREATION

Part 1

SESSION 7

The Big Question:

Is it intellectually feasible to believe that a supernatural, intelligent being (God) created the world, the universe, and all living things?

OR

Is evolution a scientific fact that has empirically and logically been proven by means of "scientific method" — observation, hypothesis, testing, and predictable results — that life is the product of a purely material universe that came into being by random chance and/or accident?

Defining our Terms:

- Micro Evolution — change only happens within species
- Darwinian Macro Evolution — change evolves from one species to the next

3 Groups within Evolution Thought

- The Classic Position — Carl Sagan
- The New Voices — Colin Patterson, Michael Denton, Philip Johnson, Michael Behe
- The Christian Evolutionists — Denis Alexander, Francis Collins, Kenneth Miller

■ IN COMMUNITY

1. At this point in your journey, what do you believe about creation and evolution? Why?

2. What was your view of creation growing up? What were you taught in church and in school about creation?

3. Have your views of creation and evolution changed over the years? If so, how and why?

4. What most stood out to you from this session?

5. How significant is this issue in your faith? Is it a total non-essential (really doesn't matter what you believe about this) or is it foundational to your faith... or is it somewhere in between?

6. In your opinion, is it possible to believe in random chance evolution and take the Bible seriously at the same time?

● ON MISSION

Take some time this week and pick up one of the recommended books on this topic and do some reading in order to further equip yourself.

Why is Creation important?

Throughout most of modern history, one of the most prominent and compelling arguments for the existence of a god (or even "the God") has been the "Argument From Design." This position suggests, quite simply, that the order and beauty of nature seems difficult – even impossible – without the aid of some supernatural Creator. Indeed, who hasn't watched a breathtaking sunset, considered the intricacy of a colorful fall oak leaf, or looked in awe at the tiny fingers of a newborn baby and wondered, "Could this possibly happen by chance?" And it doesn't take an advanced degree in any of the sciences to observe this. Even in pre-modern times, people's surroundings were a catalyst to wonder how all this got here. And most consequently believe in some form of creation. To conclude that it "just happened" seemed like a cop-out, or at least thoughtless.

Contemporary philosophers and theologians have stated the argument like this:

1. The universe displays an incredible amount of order.

2. Either this order happened by chance or is the result of some intelligent design.

3. It cannot be by chance.

4. Therefore it must be the product of an intelligent design.

5. And since design is the product of a designer, the universe is the product of an intelligent designer.

Of course, critics of this argument say the third premise is plainly false. Turning the argument on its head, they suggest that the burden of proof is on believers to demonstrate why all of creation *cannot* be a product of pure chance. And unless and until that is demonstrated without a doubt – they contend – the Argument From Design fails.

Yet, this, itself, is not logical. It is actually up to *non-believers* to produce a reasonable alternative to the universe as the product of an intelligent creator. And "chance" is no such alternative. That's because we only understand the concept of chance because of our common perception that things generally follow a sense of order. In other words, just as "darkness" is a meaningless concept without light, and "bad" doesn't make sense if there is no good, "chance," or apparent disorder, is a meaningless concept without order. And that pure chance could have emerged on a backdrop of a marvelously ordered world would, in fact, be miraculous.[1]

---

[1] Peter Kreeft is a Boston College philosopher and theologian who wrote *Handbook of Christian Apologetics*. IVP Academic (March 22, 1994), p. 56-57. The above presentation borrows from his brilliant exposition.

Nonetheless, as the fields of biology, physics, chemistry and archaeology mature, its practitioners are proposing various new explanations for our existence and the creation around us. And often, those explanations *exclude* any reference to a supernatural, creative being. Most of these proposals use as their starting point the "naturalistic"[2] assumptions that the supernatural cannot and does not exist. Consequently, these scientists work backwards from our current reality to propose different theories for how things could have come to be, apart from God.

And once one eliminates the potential of creation by a Creator, there is no justification for moral law, accountability is illogical, and all justifiable rules disappear. Observing the same tension, Dostoyevsky remarked, "If there is no God, everything is permissible."[3] And stating it even more forcefully, William Provine, Cornell University's Distinguished Professor of Biology, quipped:

> "Naturalistic evolution [A random, undirected working without either plan or purpose] has clear consequences that Charles Darwin understood perfectly. 1) No gods exist; 2) No life after death exists; 3) No ultimate foundation for ethics exists; and 4) No ultimate meaning in life exists."[4]

So important is the concept of our universe being the product of an intelligent designer that Peter Kreeft argues, *"No idea in the history of human thought has ever made more difference than the idea of Creation."*[5] And the Psalmist agrees, in exclaiming,

> "The heavens declare the glory of God; the skies proclaim the work of his hands."[6]

---

[2] A naturalist is someone who believes that nature is all there is... Nothing supernatural, therefore, exists.

[3] In *The Brothers Karamazov*.

[4] Excerpted from, "Evolution: Free will and punishment and meaning in life," his 1998 Darwin Day Keynote Address.

[5] Kreeft, p. 106.

[6] Psalm 19:1.

Recommended Reading:

1. Dinesh D'Souza, *What's So Great About Christianity?* (especially chapter 12)

2. Francis Collins, *The Language of God: A Scientist Presents Evidence for Belief.*

3. Alister McGrath, *Science and Religion: A New Introduction.*

4. Steven Weinberg, *The First Three Minutes: A Modern View Of The Origin Of The Universe.* (This is a good book to understand an opposing view)

WHY I BELIEVE
IN CREATION

Part 2

SESSION 8

Examining the evidence for yourself:

1. _____ did life begin?

   EVOLUTION...

   "An unsupervised, impersonal, unpredictable and natural process."

   ASSOCIATION OF BIOLOGY TEACHERS

   "A random, undirected working without either plan or purpose."

   PRENTICE HALL TEXT BOOK

   CREATION...

   "In the beginning God created the heavens and the earth."

   GENESIS 1:1 (NIV)

2. _____ did life begin?

   EVOLUTION'S ANSWER:

   Pure accident, random chance.

CREATION'S ANSWER:

> God made man in His own image to share relationship with Him, glorify Him and steward the Earth.

So God created mankind in his own image, in the image of God he created them; male and female he created them.

God blessed them and said to them, "Be fruitful and increase in number; fill the earth and subdue it. Rule over the fish in the sea and the birds in the sky and over every living creature that moves on the ground."

GENESIS 1:27-28 (NIV)

He has made everything beautiful in its time. He has also set eternity in the human heart; yet no one can fathom what God has done from beginning to end.

ECCLESIASTES 3:11 (NIV)

3. How did various _____ develop?

EVOLUTION:

> A simple cell evolved to more complex plants and animals through the process of time, chance, natural selection, mutations, and survival of the fittest over a period of billions of years.

CREATION:

God created various plants, animals, kinds, and species in a harmonic balance to reflect His attributes and character.

For since the creation of the world God's invisible qualities — his eternal power and divine nature — have been clearly seen, being understood from what has been made, so that people are without excuse.

ROMANS 1:20 (NIV)

¹The heavens declare the glory of God; the skies proclaim the work of his hands. ²Day after day they pour forth speech; night after night they display knowledge. ³There is no speech or language where their voice is not heard.

PSALM 19:1-3 (NIV)

4. Which theory / claim best explains the _____?

- Darwin's admission

- Darwin's confidence of future discoveries

- The present state of fossil records

In the secular account, you are the descendent of a tiny cell of primordial protoplasm washed up on an empty beach three and a half billion years ago. You are a mere grab bag of atomic particles, a conglomeration of genetic substance. You exist on a tiny planet in a minute solar system in an empty corner of a meaningless universe. You came from nothing and you are going nowhere.

In the Christian view you are the special creation of a good and all powerful God. You are the climax of his creation. Not only is your kind unique, but you are unique among your kind. Your creator loves you so much and so intensely that he desires your companionship and affection that he gave the life of His only son that you might spend eternity with him.

WHAT'S SO GREAT ABOUT CHRISTIANITY
BY DINESH D'SOUZA

■ IN COMMUNITY

1. Read over the quote from Dinesh D'Souza. What are your thoughts on his conclusion?

2. If we are nothing more than "primordial protoplasm", what are the implications for how we approach living our lives?

3. If we are the special creation of the a good and all powerful God, what are the implications for how we approach living our lives?

4. Of Chip's four questions in this session, which one has been the biggest struggle for you? Why?

5. Ecclesiastes 3:11 (NIV) says *He has made everything beautiful in its time. He has also set eternity in the human heart; yet no one can fathom what God has done from beginning to end.*

   What does it mean that God has set "eternity" in the human heart?

6. Read Romans 1:20 and Psalm 19:1-3. The Bible says that God reveals himself through creation. For you personally, which part of creation most reveals God?

● ON MISSION

Find a place this week where you can enjoy God's creation. Take someone with you to enjoy the beauty and talk about the greatness of God's creation.

WHY I BELIEVE
IN CREATION

Part 3

SESSION 9

Examining The Evidence For Yourself (Continued from Session 8)

5. Which claim (science or scripture) best explains our most recent

   _____?

   - **In Astronomy/Physics – The Big Bang**
     Hugh Ross, *The Fingerprint of God*

   - **In the Fossil Record**
     The Cambrian Explosion, TIME, December 5, 1995

   - **In Molecular Biology**
     Michael Behe, *Darwin's Black Box*

   "If it could be demonstrated that any complex organ existed which could not possibly have been formed by numerous, successive, slight modifications, my theory would absolutely break down."

   CHARLES DARWIN, *THE ORIGIN OF SPECIES*

   - **In Genetics – DNA – Coded Information**
     Michael Denton, *Evolution: A Theory in Crisis*

   In the genetic information in DNA, in a microscopic single cell organism, if it was spelled out in English, it would equal the whole volume of the encyclopedia Britannica.

   DNA is the divine computer program that indicates there must have been a divine programmer.

   World class expert in DNA (and evolutionist) was asked "What are the chances DNA could have been formed by a random process?" His answer: "None."

■ IN COMMUNITY

1.   What was your biggest takeaway from the teaching in this session?

2.   In your opinion, which of the 5 scientific discoveries that Chip talked about during this session was least likely to happen by chance (without a creator)?

3.   Chip said that some scientists rejected the big bang theory because they said if the big bang was true it implied a moment of creation when the universe and its laws came into existence. How do you respond to that statement?

4.   Read Psalm 139:13-18. In light of what Chip shared about DNA, what part of this passage most stands out to you? Why?

5. Chip talked about the "anthropic principle" which means that the earth is perfectly suited for man to live on it. As a group, brainstorm a list of ways in which planet earth is perfectly designed for human life?

6. Chip read a quote from the Language of God which said "Our concern and care for others is an evidence of God. Of all the mysteries of human behavior, our sense of altruism and caring for others who need us, flies in the face of Darwin's teaching of survival of the fittest." In your opinion, is this a legitimate argument for creation vs. random chance? Why or why not?

● ON MISSION

Do a little homework assignment this week on DNA. Get on the internet and discover the facts about DNA and see if it makes a better case for creation or random chance evolution.

WHY I BELIEVE
IN CREATION

Part 4

SESSION 10

Examining The Evidence For Yourself (Continued from Session 9)

- **In Genetic Codes – Sequencing The Human Genome**
  Francis Collins, *The Language of God*

6. Which theory / claim has had the greatest _____
    benefit to mankind?

    - Darwinism and Humanism – God dethroned

    - Darwinism and Morality – Relative truth birthed

    - Darwinism and Racism, Nazism, Sexism

7. Which theory/claim reflects most accurately the laws of
    _____ research?

    - Great scientist's historical presuppositions

    - Law of Cause and Effect

    - Law of Thermodynamics

8. Which theory / claim has the best _____
    track record for their position?

    - Our "Common Ancestor" - undiscovered

    - The multiple "Missing Links" – discredited

- The Biblical archeological track record

    Sir William Ramsey — an archeologist who went to Israel to disprove the Bible "The Bible's historical and archeological accuracy are unsurpassed. No discovery has disproved the biblical accounts to date."

■ IN COMMUNITY

1. In your opinion, "Is evolution the 'airtight' scientific fact as we have been taught?"

2. What stood out to you the most from Chip's teaching in this session?

3. Has your view changed or grown as a result of looking at the data presented in these sessions on creation? If so, how?

4. In this session Chip made a connection between Darwinian evolution and situational ethics/moral relativity. Do you agree with his conclusion that the two are connected? Why or why not?

5. The second law of thermodynamics says that everything is moving from order to chaos, not the other way around. Give some examples of this and explain why this is a problem for evolution?

6. Read Isaiah 40:12-31. As you read about our "creator" God, what verse most stands out to you? Why?

● ON MISSION

Have a conversation this week with a friend and share with them some of what you have been learning about the issue of creation vs. Darwinian evolution.

Why is Creation reasonable?

In academic scholarship today, it is eminently common to reject any and all forms of the supernatural, in favor of a completely naturalistic interpretation of creation, history, biology and even our daily circumstances. However, while there are plenty of theories of creation that eliminate reliance upon a Creator, none are universally accepted as fact.

Perhaps the most popular naturalistic explanation of our world hinges on Charles Darwin's discovery that species appear to evolve over time. Richard Dawkins, the famous atheist, often exults that the great achievement of Darwin's theory is that it shows how creatures that appear to be designed have in fact evolved according to the pressures of chance and survival.[1] Francisco Ayala contends that because of Darwin's discovery "we are without any need to resort to a Creator."[2] And yet, the fact that we share the majority of our DNA with the animal kingdom says nothing about how animals and humans originated. Only that the materials used are shared.[3] Dinesh D'Souza counters that, "We may have common ancestors with the animals, but we are *glorified* animals."

Indeed, there is ample evidence to be confident that life is the result of more than random combinations of atoms that assembled themselves to create everything that is, was and ever will be. In his book, *A Brief History of Time,* physicist Stephen Hawking suggests that even the slightest modification of our planet's location, rotation, and countless other measurements, would unravel things such that the universe would not and could not exist.[4] And, the awesomeness of design is not limited to things on such a grand scale. D'Souza reminds us that, "The simplest living cell is one of the most complicated structures on earth, containing with it more information than multiple sets of the *Encyclopedia Britannica*."[5] And finally, the existence of morality presents an extreme challenge to atheistic theories. For if we're simply the result of meaningless chance, from where does the universal sense of good and bad come? Most atheists acknowledge that this is a conundrum and hole in their hypothesis.

---

[1] D'Souza, Dinesh. *What's So Great About Christianity?* Regnery Publishing, Inc. (2007), p. 24.
[2] Ayala, Francisco. *Darwin's gift to science and religion.* Joseph Henry Press (April 23, 2007), p. 42.
[3] Which is completely consistent with the Biblical account of human creation as noted in Genesis 2:7.
[4] Hawking, Stephen. *A Brief History of Time.* Bantam Books. (1996), P. 12-13.
[5] D'Souza, p. 148.

That said, though the evidence for Creation is strong, Christians are not necessarily agreed on how it all happened. The most popular theory over the past millennium is often called Young Earth theory. Those who hold this view believe that God created the world in six 24-hour days in the last 6,000 to 10,000 years, taking a very literal interpretation of the first chapters of the book of Genesis. Young Earth Creationists are often suspicious of science and its hold on the academic and intellectual environment, believing that any scientific evidence supporting evolution or other theories contrary to a literal interpretation of the biblical account is simply a misunderstanding of the scientific evidence or even a theological predisposition against the supernatural.

Another group of Christians take what is called the Old Earth position. They acknowledge that science provides some compelling evidence that the earth is older than six or ten thousand years. That when the Bible refers to six days of creation, based on the translation of the Hebrew word, "yom," it actually refers to six eras or epochs or seasons, rather than literal days. However, Old Earth Creationists generally remain skeptical about evolutionary development.

A third group of Christians takes a position that is called Theistic Evolution. As the term implies, these people accept the majority of scientific evidence that suggests the earth is older than a few thousand years, and that evolution is the biological process from which humans developed. But they still believe that God himself created and guided that process. As such, they interpret the early chapters of Genesis as more literary or poetic, rather than literal. In other words, the account expresses something true about creation, but shouldn't be taken literally or scientifically.

Obviously, these are broad generalizations and there is wide diversity within each group. But, regarding the creation story, most Christians fall into one of these three categories.

That said, we need to abide by two guiding principles in this discussion. First, we are playing out of our league. In Paul's letter to the Roman church, he cautions the young believers that the mind, knowledge and ways of God far surpass anything we can conjure.[6] And second, most important to the Biblical account of creation is the *who* and *why*, not necessarily the *what* and *how*. In other words, the Christian religion has as its focus the *Maker* of creation, not necessarily the method of creation.

---

[6] Romans 11:33-36.

Recommended Reading:

1. Dinesh D'Souza, *What's So Great About Christianity?* (especially chapter 12)

2. Francis Collins, *The Language of God: A Scientist Presents Evidence for Belief.*

3. Alister McGrath, *Science and Religion: A New Introduction.*

4. Steven Weinberg, *The First Three Minutes: A Modern View Of The Origin Of The Universe.* (A good book to understand the opposing view)

WHY I BELIEVE
IN THE GOD OF THE BIBLE

Part 1

SESSION 11

▲ BEFORE GOD (Watch the Video)

Is it intellectually feasible to believe there is one true God and if so, what are the facts?

Common Presuppositions

- "Aren't all religions essentially the same?"
  The answer is a categorical NO.

- "Does it really matter what a person believes as long as he / she is sincere and practices those beliefs?"
  The answer is a categorical YES.

> *Enter through the narrow gate. For wide is the gate and broad is the road that leads to destruction, and many enter through it. But small is the gate and narrow the road that leads to life, and only a few find it.*
>
> ───────────────────────
>
> JESUS OF NAZARETH — MATTHEW 7:13-14

7 Reasons Why I Believe in the God of the Bible:

1. The _____ Evidence
   Christianity is subject to objective verification

   - Historical Events

   - Trustworthiness of Biblical Records

   - Manuscript Evidence

   - Extra-Biblical Sources

   - Eyewitness Accounts of the Resurrection

2. The _____ Evidence
   Predictions of specific future events with 100% accuracy confirm
   authenticity.

   • The Isaiah Principle

⁶"This is what the LORD says — Israel's King and Redeemer, the LORD Almighty: I am the first and I am the last; apart from me there is no God. ⁷Who then is like me? Let him proclaim it. Let him declare and lay out before me what has happened since I established my ancient people, and what is yet to come — yes, let them foretell what will come.

ISAIAH 44:6-7 (NIV)

²⁴"This is what the LORD says — your Redeemer, who formed you in the womb: I am the LORD, the Maker of all things, who stretches out the heavens, who spreads out the earth by myself, ²⁵who foils the signs of false prophets and makes fools of diviners, who overthrows the learning of the wise and turns it into nonsense, ²⁶who carries out the words of his servants and fulfills the predictions of his messengers, who says of Jerusalem, 'It shall be inhabited,' of the towns of Judah, 'They shall be rebuilt,' and of their ruins, 'I will restore them,' ²⁷who says to the watery deep, 'Be dry, and I will dry up your streams,' ²⁸who says of Cyrus, 'He is my shepherd and will accomplish all that I please; he will say of Jerusalem, "Let it be rebuilt," and of the temple, "Let its foundations be laid."'

ISAIAH 44:24-28 (NIV)

- The Test of a Prophet

[21]You may say to yourselves, "How can we know when a message has not been spoken by the LORD?" [22]If what a prophet proclaims in the name of the LORD does not take place or come true, that is a message the LORD has not spoken. That prophet has spoken presumptuously, so do not be alarmed.

DEUTERONOMY 18:21-22 (NIV)

- The Fulfillment of Hundreds of Specific Prophecies

3. The _____ Evidence
   The triune nature of God and testimony of Scripture best answer life's most timeless questions.

   - The Problem of Unity and Diversity

   - The Problem of Evil and Justice

   - The Origin of Personality

   - The Enigma of Man

■ IN COMMUNITY

1. What insight from this week's teaching most grabbed your attention? Explain why.

2. If someone told you that they think Christianity is narrow-minded and intolerant, how would you respond to them?

3. If you were asked the question "Why are you betting your life on Jesus Christ and Christianity?" What would you say?

4. What would you say to the person who says that Jesus is just one of many ways to heaven?

5. Read again the passage of Scripture from Isaiah 44:24-28. If you had to summarize this passage in one sentence, what would you say?

_____

_____

_____

6. When having conversations about the controversial issues in this series, what are some things we "shouldn't" do?

_____

_____

_____

● ON MISSION
_____

Share some of what you are learning with one person you think needs to hear these truths.

WHY I BELIEVE
IN THE GOD OF THE BIBLE

Part 2

SESSION 12

7 Reasons Why I Believe In The God Of The Bible (Continued from Session 11)

4. The evidence of _____
   The long-term fruitfulness and greatness of Israel and the church argues for its truthfulness.

   • The great nation of Israel

   • The great laws of Israel

   • The mustard seed conspiracy of Jesus

   • The liberation of women, slaves, caste systems, basis of jurisprudence, economic impact, care for the poor, orphans, widows, and the disenfranchised of every age

5. The _____ evidence
   The teachings of Jesus and the New Testament work in real life!

   • They promote healthy relationships, strong marriages, honest business, positive parenting, racial reconciliation, cultural kindness, and champion the value and dignity of all humans regardless of creed, race, sex, nationality, or orientation.

6. The evidence of _____
   God's chief messenger (Jesus) and message (grace) stand in contrast to all religions and religious teaching.

   • The Messenger: Jesus — Deity (John 1:1-18), Sinless (John 12), Creator (Colossians 1:15), Savior (John 3:16), His Outrageous Claim (John 14:6).

   • The Message: Grace — the unconditional, unmerited love of God toward every human being that compels Him to forgive and reconcile them to Himself (all who are willing) based solely on the work of Christ on the cross, not on any religious performance or righteous works of their own... It's a "gift." (Ephesians 2:8-9).

7. The _____ evidence
    The millions of "changed lives" in the last 2,000 years argue
    experientially that Jesus is alive and is who He said He is.

Three reasons why don't people believe?

1. _____ Romans 10:14-15

> [14]How, then, can they call on the one they have not
> believed in? And how can they believe in the one of
> whom they have not heard? And how can they hear
> without someone preaching to them? [15]And how can
> anyone preach unless they are sent? As it is written:
> "How beautiful are the feet of those who bring good
> news!"
>
> ROMANS 10:14-15 (NIV)

2. _____ John 12:42-43

> [42]Yet at the same time many even among the leaders
> believed in him. But because of the Pharisees they
> would not openly acknowledge their faith for fear they
> would be put out of the synagogue; [43]for they loved
> human praise more than praise from God.
>
> JOHN 12:42-43 (NIV)

3. _____ John 3:19-20

> *¹⁹This is the verdict: Light has come into the world, but people loved darkness instead of light because their deeds were evil. ²⁰Everyone who does evil hates the light, and will not come into the light for fear that his deeds will be exposed.*
>
> ---
>
> **JOHN 3:19-20 (NIV)**

■ IN COMMUNITY

1. What insight or new learning did you get from this week's teaching?

   _____

   _____

   _____

2. Which of the topics in this series most impacted you? Why? (The Resurrection, ... The Bible, ... Life After Death, ...Creation, ... The God of the Bible.)

   _____

   _____

   _____

3. Chip talked about the evidence of positive impact in our world. How have you seen God at work and positive impact of Christians in your own local community?

4. As a group, brainstorm a list of characteristics that sets Jesus apart from all other religious leaders.

5. Chip shared some reasons why people don't believe. Before you came to Christ, what was the barrier you had to get over?

6. Chip talked about believing in the existential evidence for believing in God... millions of people around the world who have had their lives changed by Jesus. Spend some time sharing as a group how Jesus has personally impacted your life.

● ON MISSION

Consider inviting a few friends to go through this study with you. By hosting this series you will reinforce what you've been learning and you will help your friends deal with some of the biggest and toughest questions of the Christian faith.

Why is the exclusive nature of the Christian faith important?

With the advent of various modern technologies, such as the telephone, television and the internet, it seems the world has gotten smaller. And as our world has "shrunk," our knowledge of people around the world has exploded exponentially. We know more details about more people than ever before. In fact, just a few generations ago, the furthest one might travel in their entire lives would likely be only a few hundred miles. And the average person's exposure to people unlike themselves would be minimal. Now, typical fifth graders in America can not only name a hundred or more countries around the world, but they can also detail and maybe even picture their typical foods, jobs, transportation methods, style of homes, and even their topography. Indeed, 24-hours per day, we can turn on the television or surf the web for up-to-the-minute news about people halfway around the world.

As this transition has progressed, most people have also become far more informed about religions around the world. Formerly, people of another faith were simply "other," or maybe even "pagans." Today, they're Muslims, Hindus, Buddhists, Jews, New Agers, Spiritists, Agnostics, Atheists and even Apathetics (ie. those who don't care). What's more – no longer are these faceless people somewhere "out there," across the ocean. But they're right here; they're our neighbors, friends, co-workers, classmates and even family members. And that makes conversation about various faiths difficult, because it's personal, intimate and relational.

As we've learned more about other religions, it's interesting to discover how many similarities there are between them. Most have a central god who's all-powerful and somehow involved in day-to-day life. This god usually doles out blessings based on good choices and right living, or wrath based on bad choices or wicked living. In a few cases, these various gods begin to look astonishingly similar.

And this begs the question: are we all describing different paths to the same place? Could we all be using our indigenous language and cultural norms to describe the same deity? Is it possible that we're all climbing the same mountain to pursue our country's or culture's or family's deity? And when we reach the summit, might we bump into one another only to discover that we had all taken different routes to arrive at the same place? It would certainly make things easier. After all, most modern conflicts are religiously based, right? And who wants to look their neighbors, friends or co-workers in the eye and tell them that your god is the right one and their god is not?

This type of thinking usually leads to two conclusions:

1. It's ok to "mix & match" our faith; and

2. We're all worshipping the same god who's been shaped by our cultural upbringing. Therefore, it doesn't matter which religion you choose since they all communicate the same things and lead to the same place.

Indeed, in this day and age, many people would prefer to do away with exclusive claims to anything – especially religion – considering them to be arrogant or closed-minded. The only problem is that few religions, Christianity included, allow this. For example, this is how far one Muslim scholar is willing to crack the door to other religions: "It is a fundamental belief of Muslims that Islam is not only a divinely revealed religion from God, but rather that it is the only acceptable religion and the sole legitimate path to His pleasure."[1] And, Jesus, himself, proclaimed some rather narrow criteria: "No one comes to the Father except through me."[2]

In other words, while it might make things easier if we could simply pick a little "religion" from here and a little from there, that's simply dishonest. To pick and choose from each of them is to be disingenuous to all of them. And the reality is the similarities between Christianity and the other religions are not as numerous as one might think. In fact, the differences far outweigh the similarities. Most religions can be described as humanity's effort to reach God. But Christianity is, conversely, God's effort – through Christ – to reach and restore humanity.

So, if we cannot "mix & match" our faiths, and if it's not possible to claim that all religions lead to the same place, then the million-dollar question is, "Which one is the right one?"[3] And, in the end, Christianity is the only religion whose messenger claimed to be one with God, lived a sinless life, and predicted and then fulfilled his own death and resurrection. It's also the only religion that provides a comprehensive solution to humanity's sin problem. Ultimately, it's the only religion where God takes the initiative in extending His unconditional, unmerited love to every human being, in an act of immeasurable grace.[4]

---

[1] http://islamhd.wordpress.com/2008/02/12/salvific-exclusivity/. Also see Surah Ale-Imran 3:85 states, "So whoever seeks a religion other than Islam, it shall not be accepted from him, and he shall be a loser in the Hereafter."

[2] John 14:6.

[3] Of course, all of them could be wrong. But all of them cannot be right.

[4] Indeed, the staggering beauty of Christianity is not its exclusivity, but instead, God's gracious inclusivity.

Additional Resources:

1. Dinesh D'Souza, *What's So Amazing About Christianity?* (especially chapter 25)

2. C.S. Lewis, *What Christians Believe,* (chapter 1, an excerpt of Mere Christianity, I believe)

3. Tim Keller, *The Reason for God: Belief in an Age of Skepticism.* (chapter 1)

4. Gregory MacDonald, *All Shall Be Well.* (For a contrary view, this is an exploration of "Christian Universalism" over the past 2,000 years.)

LEADER'S NOTES

GROUP AGREEMENT

People come to groups with a variety of different expectations. The purpose of a group agreement is simply to make sure everyone is on the same page and that we have some common expectations.

The following Group Agreement is a tool to help you discuss specific guidelines during your first meeting. Modify anything that does not work for your group, then be sure to discuss the questions in the section called Our Game Plan. This will help you to have an even greater group experience!

WE AGREE TO THE FOLLOWING PRIORITIES

- **Take the Bible Seriously** — To seek to understand and apply God's truth in the Bible

- **Group Attendance** — To give priority to the group meeting (Call if I am going to be absent or late.)

- **Safe Environment** — To create a safe place where people can be heard and feel loved (no snap judgments or simple fixes)

- **Respectful Discussion** — To speak in a respectful and honoring way to our mate and others in the group

- **Be Confidential** — To keep anything that is shared strictly confidential and within the group

- **Spiritual Health** — To give group members permission to help me live a godly, healthy spiritual life that is pleasing to God

- **Building Relationships** — To get to know the other members of the group and pray for them regularly

- **Prayer** — To regularly pray with and for each other

- **Other**

OUR GAME PLAN

- What will we do for refreshments?

  _____

  _____

  _____

- What will we do about childcare?

  _____

  _____

  _____

- What day and time will we meet?

  _____

  _____

  _____

- Where will we meet?

  _____

  _____

  _____

- How long will we meet each week?

  _____

  _____

  _____

BEFORE THE GROUP ARRIVES

1. **Be prepared.** Your personal preparation can make a huge difference in the quality of the group experience. We strongly suggest previewing both the DVD teaching by Chip Ingram and the study guide.

2. **Pray for your group members by name.** Ask God to use your time together to touch the heart of every person in your group. Expect God to challenge and change people as a result of this study.

3. **Provide refreshments.** There's nothing like food to help a group relax and connect with each other. For the first week, we suggest you prepare a snack, but after that, ask other group members to bring the food so that they share in the responsibilities of the group and make a commitment to return.

4. **Relax.** Don't try to imitate someone else's style of leading a group. Lead the group in a way that fits your style and temperament. Remember that people may feel nervous showing up for a small group study, so put them at ease when they arrive. Make sure to have all the details covered prior to your group meeting, so that once people start arriving, you can focus on them.

▲ BEFORE GOD (Watch the Video)

1. **Get the video ready.** Each video session on the DVD will have 3 components. The first 2 minutes Chip will introduce this week's topic Then, you will watch the actual teaching content that Chip taught in front of a live audience. This portion of the video will be roughly 20-30 minutes in length. Finally, Chip will then share some closing thoughts and set up the discussion time for your group.

2. **Test the equipment.** Be sure to test your video equipment ahead of time and make sure you have located this week's lesson on the DVD menu. The video segments flow from one right into the next. So, once you start the session, you won't have to stop the video until Chip has finished his closing thoughts and prepared the group for the first discussion question.

3. **Have ample materials.** Before you start the video, also make sure everyone has their own copy of the study guide. Encourage the group to open to this week's session and follow along with the teaching. There is an outline in the study guide with an opportunity to fill in the outline.

4. **Arrange the room.** Set up the chairs in the room so that everyone can see the television. And, arrange the room in such a way that it is conducive to discussion.

■ IN COMMUNITY

Here are some guidelines for leading the discussion time:

1. **Make this a discussion, not a lecture.** Resist the temptation to do all the talking, and to answer your own questions. Don't be afraid of a few moments of silence while people formulate their answers.

   And don't feel like you need to have all the answers. There is nothing wrong with simply saying "I don't know the answer to that, but I'll see if I can find an answer this week".

2. **Encourage everyone to participate.** Don't let one person dominate, but also don't pressure quieter members to speak during the first couple of sessions. Because this is a doctrinal series, it may be intimidating for some to share their thoughts and ideas. Be patient. Ask good follow up questions and be sensitive to delicate issues.

3. **Affirm people's participation and input.** If an answer is clearly wrong, ask "What led you to that conclusion?" or ask what the rest of the group thinks. If a disagreement arises, don't be too quick to shut it down! The discussion can draw out important perspectives, and if you can't resolve it there, offer to research it further and return to the issue next week.

   However, if someone goes on the offensive and engages in personal attack, you will need to step in as the leader. In the midst of spirited discussion, we must also remember that people are fragile and there is no place for disrespect.

4. **Detour when necessary.** If an important question is raised that is not in the study guide, take time to discuss it. Also, if someone shares something personal and emotional, take time for them. Stop and pray for them right then. Allow the Holy Spirit room to maneuver, and follow his prompting when the discussion changes direction.

5. **Subgroup.** One of the principles of small group life is "when numbers go up, sharing goes down". So, if you have a large group, sometimes you may want to split up into groups of 4-6 for the discussion time. This is a great way to give everyone, even the quieter members, a chance to share. Choose someone in the group to guide each of the smaller groups through the discussion. This involves others in the leadership of the group, and provides an opportunity for training new leaders.

6. **Prayer.** Be sensitive to the fact that some people in your group may be uncomfortable praying out loud. As a general rule, don't call on people to pray unless you have asked them ahead of time or have heard them pray in public. But this can also be a time to help people build their confidence to pray in a group. Consider having prayer times that ask people to just say a word or sentence of thanks to God.

● ON MISSION

These simple suggestions will help the group apply the lesson. Be sure and leave adequate time to talk about these practical applications of the lesson. Most of the weekly assignments involve an action step that will encourage the group to put into practice what they are learning. Occasionally ask people if they have been working on these assignments and what the results have been.

PRAYER AND PRAISE

One of the most important things you can do in your group is to pray with and for each other. Write down each other's concerns here so you can remember to pray for these requests during the week!

Use the Follow Up box to record an answer to a prayer or to write down how you might want to follow up with the person making the request. This could be a phone call, an e-mail, or a card. Your personal concern will mean a lot!

PERSON	PRAYER REQUEST	FOLLOW UP

PERSON	PRAYER REQUEST	FOLLOW UP

PERSON	PRAYER REQUEST	FOLLOW UP

PERSON	PRAYER REQUEST	FOLLOW UP

GROUP ROSTER

NAME	HOME PHONE	EMAIL

WHAT'S NEXT?

More Group Studies from Chip Ingram:

BALANCING LIFE'S DEMANDS
Biblical Priorities for a Busy Life

Busy, tired and stressed out? Learn how to put "first things first" and find peace in the midst of pressure and adversity.

BIO
How to Become An Authentic Disciple of Jesus

Unlock the Biblical DNA for spiritual momentum by examining the questions at the heart of true spirituality.

CULTURE SHOCK
A Biblical Response to Today's Most Divisive Issues

Bring light—not heat—to divisive issues, such as abortion, homosexuality, sex, politics, the environment, politics and more.

DOING GOOD
What Happens When Christians Really Live Like Christians

This series clarifies what Doing Good will do in you and then through you, for the benefit of others and the glory of God.

EFFECTIVE PARENTING IN A DEFECTIVE WORLD
Raising Kids that Stand Out from the Crowd

Packed with examples and advice for raising kids, this series presents Biblical principles for parenting that still work today.

EXPERIENCING GOD'S DREAM FOR YOUR MARRIAGE
Practical Tools for a Thriving Marriage

Examine God's design for marriage and the real life tools and practices that will transform it for a lifetime.

FIVE LIES THAT RUIN RELATIONSHIPS
Building Truth-Based Relationships

Uncover five powerful lies that wreck relationships and experience the freedom of understanding how to recognize God's truth.

Watch previews and order at livingontheedge.org or 888.333.6003

THE GENIUS OF GENEROSITY
Lessons from a Secret Pact Between Friends
The smartest financial move you can make is to invest in God's Kingdom. Learn His design for wise giving and generous living.

GOD AS HE LONGS FOR YOU TO SEE HIM
Seeing God With 20/20 Vision
A deeper look at seven attributes of God's character that will change the way you think, pray and live.

GOOD TO GREAT IN GOD'S EYES
10 Practices Great Christians Have in Common
If you long for spiritual breakthrough, take a closer look at ten powerful practices that will rekindle a fresh infusion of faith.

HEAVEN
It's Not What You Think
Chip Ingram digs into scripture to reveal what heaven will be like, what we'll do there, and how we're to prepare for eternity today.

HOLY AMBITION
Turning God-Shaped Dreams Into Reality
Do you long to turn a God-inspired dream into reality? Learn how God uses everyday believers to accomplish extraordinary things.

HOUSE OR HOME: MARRIAGE EDITION
God's Blueprint for a Great Marriage
Get back to the blueprint and examine God's plan for marriages that last for a lifetime.

HOUSE OR HOME: PARENTING EDITION
God's Blueprint for Biblical Parenting
Timeless truths about God's blueprint for parenting, and the potential to forever change the trajectory of your family.

Watch previews and order at livingontheedge.org or 888.333.6003

THE INVISIBLE WAR
The Believer's Guide to Satan, Demons and Spiritual Warfare
Learn how to clothe yourself with God's "spiritual armor" and be confident of victory over the enemy of your soul.

LOVE, SEX AND LASTING RELATIONSHIPS
God's Prescription to Enhance Your Love Life
Do you believe in "true love"? Discover a better way to find love, stay in love, and build intimacy that lasts a lifetime.

REBUILDING YOUR BROKEN WORLD
How God Puts Broken Lives Back Together
Learn how God can reshape your response to trials and bring healing to broken relationships and difficult circumstances.

SPIRITUAL SIMPLICITY
Doing Less • Loving More
If you crave simplicity and yearn for peace this study is for you. Spiritual simplicity can only occur when we do less and love more.

TRANSFORMED
The Miracle of Life Change
Ready to make a change? Explore God's process of true transformation and learn to spot barriers that hold you back from receiving God's best.

TRUE SPIRITUALITY
Becoming a Romans 12 Christian
We live in a world that is activity-heavy and relationship-light. Learn the next steps toward True Spirituality.

WHY I BELIEVE
Answers to Life's Most Difficult Question
Can miracles be explained? Is there really a God? There are solid, logical answers about claims of the Christian faith.

YOUR DIVINE DESIGN
Discover, Develop and Deploy Your Spiritual Gifts
How has God uniquely wired you? Discover God's purpose for spiritual gifts and how to identify your own.

Watch previews and order at livingontheedge.org or 888.333.6003